Developing Literacy POETRY

READING AND WRITING ACTIVITIES FOR THE LITERACY HOUR

Christine Moorcroft
Series consultant Ray Barker

A & C BLACK

Contents

Repetition and choruses

Word-play

Acknowledgements
The author and publishers are grateful for permission to reproduce the following:
'The Bird' by Tony Mitton © 1996 Tony Mitton; 'Mudlarks' from *Out and About* © 1988, 1998 Shirley Hughes. Reproduced by permission of the publisher Walker Books Ltd., London.

Reprinted 2002
Published 2001 by
A & C Black Publishers Limited
37 Soho Square, London W1D 3QZ
www.acblack.com

ISBN 0-7136-5866-5

The author and publishers would like to thank Ray Barker, Madeleine Madden, Kim Pérez and Julia Tappin for their advice in producing this series of books.

A CIP catalogue record for this book is available from the British Library.

A & C Black uses paper produced with elemental chlorine-free pulp, harvested from managed sustainable forests.
Printed in Great Britain by Caligraving Ltd, Thetford, Norfolk.

Introduction

Developing Literacy: Poetry is a series of seven photocopiable activity books for the Literacy Hour. Each book provides a range of poetry activities for the Literacy Hour, and supports the teaching of reading and writing skills at text, sentence and word levels. The books contain more than enough ideas for the year for which they are intended, and provide teachers with a range of activities to select from.

The activities are designed to be carried out in the time allocated to independent work and incorporate strategies that encourage independent learning – for example, ways in which children can evaluate their own work or that of a partner. Most children will be able to carry out the activities on their own, but it is assumed that an adult will read the instructions to or with the younger children.

The activities in **Year R** encourage children to:

- re-read familiar poems with predictable and repeated patterns;
- develop their enjoyment of familiar and new rhymes, jingles, verses and poems;
- notice the structures of poems they read and understand how the language of poetry works;
- play with words, sounds, rhymes and rhythms;
- create their own poems and rhymes with the aid of the frameworks provided.

The National Literacy Strategy and poetry

The National Literacy Strategy *Framework for Teaching* encourages teachers to read all kinds of poetry and verse with children, including playground chants, nursery rhymes, action rhymes, advertisements and jingles as well as more formal poetry. The text-level objectives include teaching *about* poetry: the different types of poetry, the devices used by poets, the 'messages' of poems and even the shapes of poems, plus many of the technical terms associated with poetry. Research also indicates that the ability to appreciate rhyme and rhythm has a positive effect on children's learning to read and spell, and that several word-level objectives can be successfully taught *through* poetry: the use of

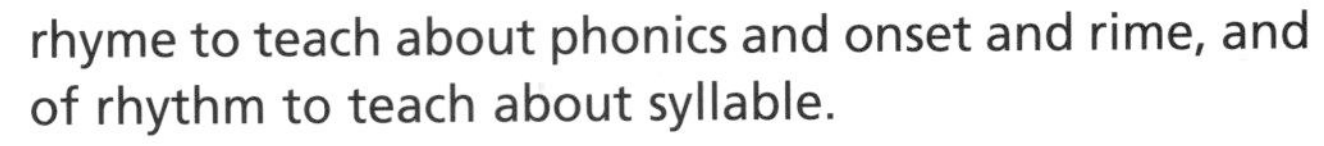

rhyme to teach about phonics and onset and rime, and of rhythm to teach about syllable.

However, teachers should not lose sight of the fun of poetry – the 'playing with words' of poets like Roger McGough and the clever use of humour by poets like Charles Causley and E V Rieu. In poetry, children can ignore the rules of grammar and put words together in new ways. And, as with other kinds of writing, the children learn from the experts. The teacher's role is to help the children to recognise a particular form of poetry and identify and practise the devices used by poets so that they can use them in their own poems.

Using poetry in the Literacy Hour

This book focuses on the independent part of the Literacy Hour, but the notes on pages 6–8 and on the activity pages suggest a variety of ways in which to introduce poetry lessons, present whole-class activities and use plenary sessions to conclude the lessons. Teachers will find it useful to vary their approaches, and could also try some of the following, as appropriate for their year group:

- playing professional tape-recordings of poems;
- choral speaking by individuals, small or large groups, and the whole class;
- learning poems a line or two at a time (varying the tone and expression as appropriate);
- reciting poems which have been learned;
- enacting, miming or singing poems;
- listing rhymes and alliterative or onomatopoeic words;
- clapping or stamping rhythms and even moving the whole body (jumping, walking and so on);
- making lists of words on a topic;
- composing poems as a group or class;
- holding small-group discussions and open forums during which the children discuss poems they have read or written.

Listening to poems

This book includes poems which need to be read to the children. By listening to poems that they would be unable to read for themselves, the children can learn to enjoy the ideas, stories and feelings expressed in such poems, as well as the sounds, rhymes and rhythms. This lays the foundations on which they can model their own poems. Listening to the poets themselves or actors reading aloud can be of special value in helping the children to enjoy a poem as well as learning how to read poetry aloud themselves. School television programmes on poetry could be used, as could commercially available tapes (tapes of nursery rhymes are particularly suitable for this age group). At the same time, giving the children the printed work to follow enables them to memorise some of the words, even if they cannot read them, and to recognise them when they come across them again.

Reading poems aloud

Several activities in this book ask the children themselves to read poems aloud (both their own and those of other poets). This helps them to appreciate the poem's meaning, atmosphere and rhythm; and in the case of their own poems, to think of changes which might improve them. Sometimes, the notes that accompany an activity suggest different ways in which the poems can be read aloud (for example, asking individuals, pairs, or small or large groups to read the parts of different characters or individual lines, groups of lines, verses and choruses). The way in which a poem is spoken can also make a valuable contribution to the children's understanding, appreciation and enjoyment of it, so you might experiment with different methods, depending on the poem: for example, a poem with a quiet atmosphere might be spoken using a combination of solo voices and hushed combined voices; the rhythm of a train might be created by having one group beginning to read a line while another group is finishing the previous line.

Memorising poems

Many of the activities suggest that the children memorise a poem, rhyme or verse. When children memorise poetry, they increase their vocabulary and develop the skill of using it expressively; they build up a rich store of creative ways in which words can be used, and begin to use the words themselves. To help the children to memorise a poem, read it aloud and then repeat it, encouraging them to join in. Either display an enlarged copy of the poem, or work with a small group of children who each have their own copy to follow. Read a line, then cover it and ask the children to repeat the line, gradually building up the number of lines covered until the children can recite the entire poem.

The following mnemonic appears in several activities to remind the children how they can learn a poem:

Organisation

None of the activities requires much in the way of additional resources besides scissors, glue, word-banks and simple dictionaries. Other materials are specified in the teachers' notes on the pages.

Extension activities

Most of the activity sheets end with a challenge (**Now try this!**) which reinforces and extends the children's learning and provides the teacher with an opportunity for assessment. These more challenging activities might be appropriate for only a few children; it is not expected that the whole class should complete all of them. On some pages there is space for the children to complete the extension activities, but others will require a notebook or separate sheet of paper.

Notes on the activities

The notes below expand upon those that are provided at the bottom of most activity pages. They give ideas and suggestions for making the most of the activity sheet, including suggestions for the whole-class introduction and the plenary session or for follow-up work using an adapted version of the activity. To help teachers select appropriate learning experiences for their pupils, the activities are grouped into sections within each book, but the pages need not be presented in the order in which they appear, unless otherwise stated.

Action poems

The activities in this section encourage the children to enact rhymes they hear or read. They also help them to appreciate the different rhythms of the poems and rhymes they hear.

Lullaby (page 9). This poem could be read as part of a collection of lullabies, with the children following the rhythm of the poem by moving a finger along the rocker of the cradle. They could make large paintings of lines to show the rhythm of a lullaby or they might paint pictures showing different types of rhythm: for example, a lively dance, a trotting horse, a speeding car or a bouncing ball. Compare the different paintings to guess the rhythms described.

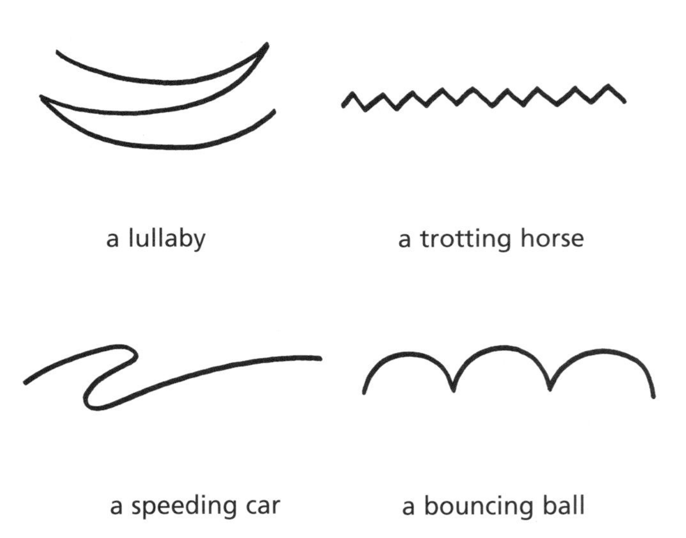

a lullaby — a trotting horse

a speeding car — a bouncing ball

Ride-a-cock-horse (page 10). This poem could be read as part of a collection of 'trotting' poems, with the children following the rhythm of the poem by 'trotting' their fingers along pairs of hoof-prints. If the materials are prepared beforehand, they could make potato or sponge prints of the hoof-prints while they recite the 'trotting' poems, or create the rhythm using percussion instruments.

See-saw, Margery Daw (pages 11–12). To introduce the 'see-saw' rhythm, show the children how to enact a see-saw by sitting in pairs on the floor with their feet touching, holding hands and rocking backwards and forwards. They could recite the rhyme as they go. They could also recite the rhyme (and their own versions of it) while moving model people up and down on ready-made see-saws or ones made from construction material.

Pat-a-cake, pat-a-cake (page 13). The children first clap their hands with the teacher as he or she reads the rhyme. Once they can clap their hands to the 'patting' rhythm, introduce other short poems and rhymes with a similar rhythm. The children could learn them and take turns to recite them, stopping and asking the rest of the class which word they have stopped on.

A hand mime (page 14). This page is designed to be read with a group or with the whole class. The pictures help the children to read and memorise the rhyme; they could do this with a partner. The children could make up their own hand mimes (which need not rhyme), for example:

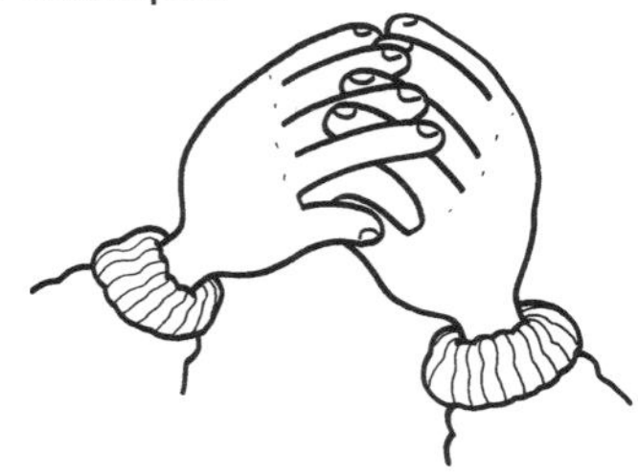

Here is the lady's garden,

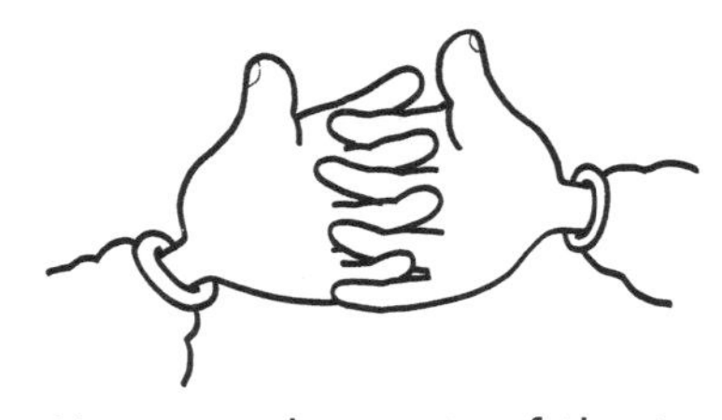

Here are the roots of the trees;

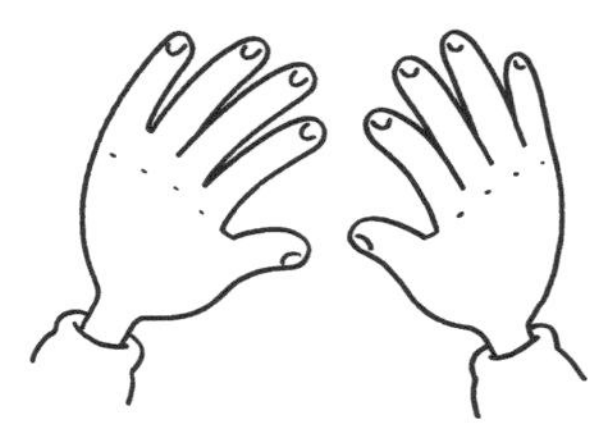

Here are the branches,

And here are the leaves.

The hand mimes could be performed in a 'shadow theatre': the children perform the hand actions behind a thin white cloth, such as a sheet, on to which a bright light is shone from behind them. The hands cast shadows on to the sheet which can be seen from the other side. **Do not let the children look directly into the light.**

A finger rhyme and **Finger puppets** (pages 15–16). After reading the rhyme and miming the actions, the children could choose a line to mime for a partner to identify and recite. In the extension activity they could use different finger puppets and change the word 'fly' to 'run', 'creep', 'slide' and so on. They could also use these finger puppets as size-templates for making up their own. The simplest way to cut out the finger holes is to fold them into semi-circles before cutting (see picture on right).

The bird (page 17). The pictures help the children to read the poem, and the actions help them to memorise it. They could take turns to do the actions while other children recite the appropriate line.

The cat and **The elephant** (pages 18–19). These are based on **The bird** (page 17). The children make up poems in a similar format but about different animals.

Mix a pancake (page 20). This activity develops the children's appreciation of the rhythm of poems; they could compare this rhythm with those of other poems and rhymes, such as *Pat-a-cake, pat-a-cake* (see page 13).

Ring-a-ring o'roses (page 21). Most children will know this nursery rhyme well, and should easily think up alternative endings even if they cannot write them. Examples they might come up with (or which the teacher could suggest) include: 'We all jump up', 'We all roll over', 'We all run fast' and 'We all stand still'. The children could take turns to tell the others what to do after 'A-tishoo'.

Question-and-answer poems

Many poems, chants and nursery rhymes have the format of 'question-and-answer'. In this section there are activities which help the children to recognise this structure, and to substitute questions and answers.

Baa, baa, Black Sheep (page 22). This is another familiar nursery rhyme which most children will know. With the help of the pictures, they should be able to recognise each part of it. Ask them what question the black sheep is being asked and how many people will get a bag of wool. The children could draw two of the scenes from this page to form part of a 'Baa, baa, Black Sheep' book in the shape of a sheep.

What are children made of? and **What are they made of?** (pages 23–25). The 'question-and-answer' arrangement of this rhyme makes it suitable for splitting into parts for groups or individuals to recite.

What's the time, Mr Wolf? (page 26). This simple poem has a repeating pattern with which the children soon become familiar. They could make up a variation by adding to the replies: for example, 'One o'clock – lunchtime' (the 'wolf' chases the 'sheep'), 'Four o'clock – time for football'.

Counting and alphabet poems

The poems, rhymes and chants in this section can be used to support work in mathematics as well as word-level work on the recognition of words for numbers and the letters of the alphabet.

A mosquito one, a mosquito two and **Find the rhyme** (pages 27–28). These activities encourage the children to listen to the endings of words and to notice rhyme. The stamping, clapping or slapping helps them to appreciate the rhythm of the poem.

One potato, two potato (page 29). By trying out different words for foods to replace 'potato', the children also learn about rhythm and stress, even though these terms are not likely to be introduced (for example, 'cucumber' has the right number of syllables, but the stress is in the wrong place).

Eeny, meeny, miney, mo (page 30). Ask the children if they use any other rhymes for choosing things or people, or making them 'out'.

Alphabet rhymes (page 31). This activity develops the children's appreciation of rhythm and rhyme. They could build up rhyme-banks of words which rhyme with the appropriate letters. Some children might be able to change the rhyme so that it goes: a and b, Here is ..., c and d, Here is ...

Alphabet poem (pages 32–33). This activity develops the children's understanding of rhythm and rhyme and their knowledge of the alphabet. Point out that they should say the names of the letters rather than the sounds they make.

Repetition and choruses

In this section the children learn to recognise repeated language and to memorise it. Some of the activities develop their skills in recognising and predicting changes in poems with patterned language.

Ee-aye-addio (page 34). Some children may recognise this popular football song. Other possible verses for the song could begin: 'We're going to win the league', 'United are the best' and 'We're going to win'.

Polly put the kettle on (page 35). This activity focuses on repetitive language. Draw the children's attention also to the sounds of the words (the repeated 'p' and 't' sounds in the first verse, and the repeated 'k' and 't' sounds in the second verse). Their own verses, using the examples provided, could end with, 'We'd all like a bite' and 'Wet soap suds'. Some children might be able to write their rhymes.

Ee-aye-ee-aye-o (pages 36–37). This activity could be adapted to make up a new poem (for example, 'Old MacDonald had a zoo'), with appropriate animals. It asks for the conventional words for animal sounds (for example, 'cluck' and 'quack').

Word-play

The emphasis of this section is on the sounds and effects of words. It encourages the children to think of descriptive or expressive words and even to make up their own. It includes activities focusing on alliterative patterns and rhyme.

Messy mud (page 38). This prepares the children for later work on onomatopoeia: most of them will recognise the repeated 's' and 'p' sounds. Made-up words to describe mud with 'p' or 's' sounds could include: 'squerch', 'slup', 'plap'. The poem could be read aloud while playing with 'mud' made from flour mixed with water. Encourage the children to listen to the sounds made by hands (or feet, in rubber boots) slapping the mud. Their own poems could be lists of words or phrases to describe mud.

Crispy crunchy (page 39). If possible, provide pieces of celery for the children to snap while repeating the words 'crispy crunchy'. They could compare its texture with that of other 'non-crispy crunchy' foods, such as yogurt and bread.

Thump, bump (page 40). Encourage the children to use the pictures as cues for the words they cannot read. Other things which go 'thump, bump' include heavy books falling, people tramping upstairs, something falling downstairs, the beat of loud pop music.

Crazy creatures (page 41). This links with word-level work on initial consonant sounds. The children could also think of animals which begin with the same letter as their own name or those of friends.

Hop to the shop (page 42). Several other activities have featured rhyme; here rhyme is the main focus of the activity. It links with word-level work on rhyming words. The children could also make up (orally) rhymes for things they do at school: for example, write by the light, read about a seed, eat the meat, bake a cake, look at a book. Possible answers for the extension activity are: go to a show, hug a big bug, fall on a ball, drink by the sink.

Sound pictures and **Sound cards** (pages 43–44). This activity requires the children to imagine the actual sounds made by the items, rather than the conventional words for the sounds. They should be able to read the sounds cards using phonics, linking with word-level work on reading and spelling strategies.

Animal sounds and **Outdoor sounds** (pages 45–46). Point to each picture in turn and ask the children to make the sound. Can the children find that sound on the page?

Morning and night poems (pages 47–48). Examples of poems the children could make up using the cards are:

Morning
Good morning
Wake up
Brush teeth
Downstairs
Breakfast.

Night
Tea
Upstairs
Bedtime story
Brush teeth
Sleepy head
Good night.

Lullaby

- **Say the lullaby.**

  With your finger, 'rock the cradle'.

- **Draw some lines to show how the cradle rocks.**

Teachers' note Read the poem aloud with the children while they move a finger back and forth along the rocker of the cradle to the rocking rhythm of the poem. For the extension activity, the children draw lines which mimic the curve of the rocking of the cradle (see **Introduction** page 6). They should first practise 'drawing' the lines in the air with a finger.

Ride-a-cock-horse

- **Say the poem.**
  Walk your fingers along the hoof-prints.

Ride-a-cock-horse to Banbury Cross
To see a fine lady upon a white horse;
With rings on her fingers and bells on her toes,
She shall have music wherever she goes.

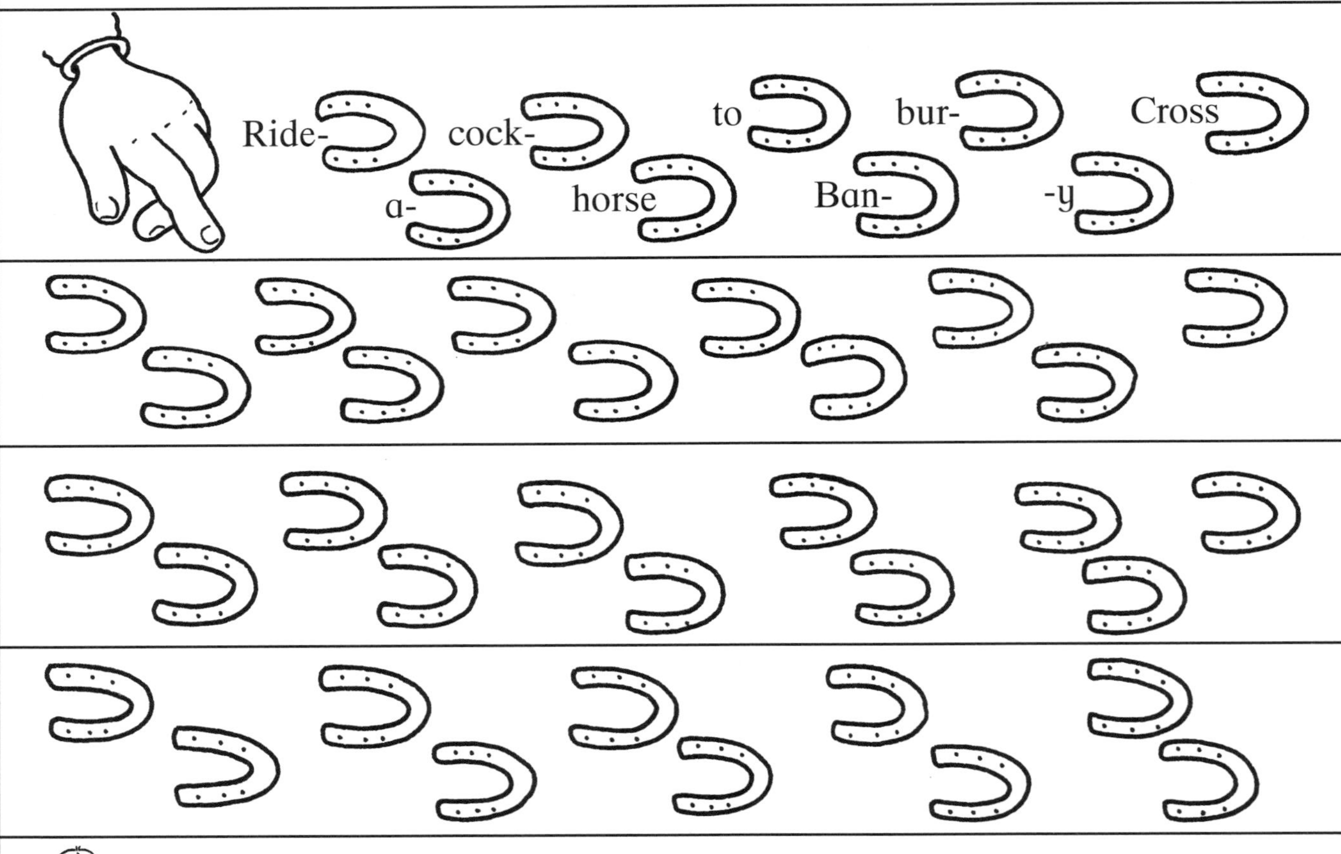

- **Make some hoof-prints for these lines.**

To market, to market, to buy a fat pig.
Home again, home again, jiggety jig.

Teachers' note Read the poem aloud while the children follow the horse's hoof-prints by walking two fingers along them (if possible, first read it while they trot around the classroom or hall). The prints are in pairs to mimic the movement of a horse. The children could also 'trot' to other rhymes with a trotting rhythm.

See-saw, Margery Daw 1

• Say the rhyme.

Move the see-saw up and down.

See-saw, Margery Daw,
Jacky shall have a new master;
He shall have but a penny a day,
Because he can't work any faster.

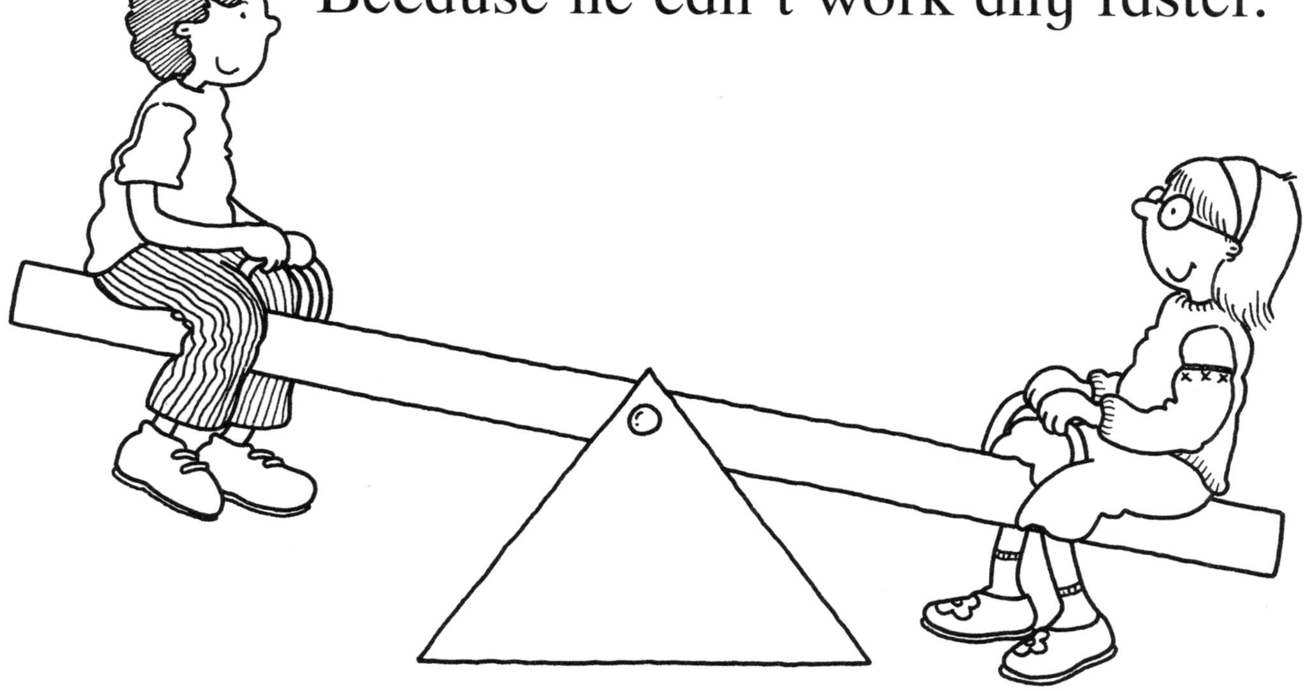

• Change the rhyme.

Say your name instead.

• Say your new rhyme.

Teachers' note The children need the see-saw on page 12. Read (or chant) the poem aloud with the children. Help them to move the see-saw up and down to the rhythm of the poem. If you have a see-saw in school they could first take turns on it while the others say the poem. In the extension activity the children should insert their own name instead of 'Jacky' and see if it fits the rhythm.

See-saw, Margery Daw 2

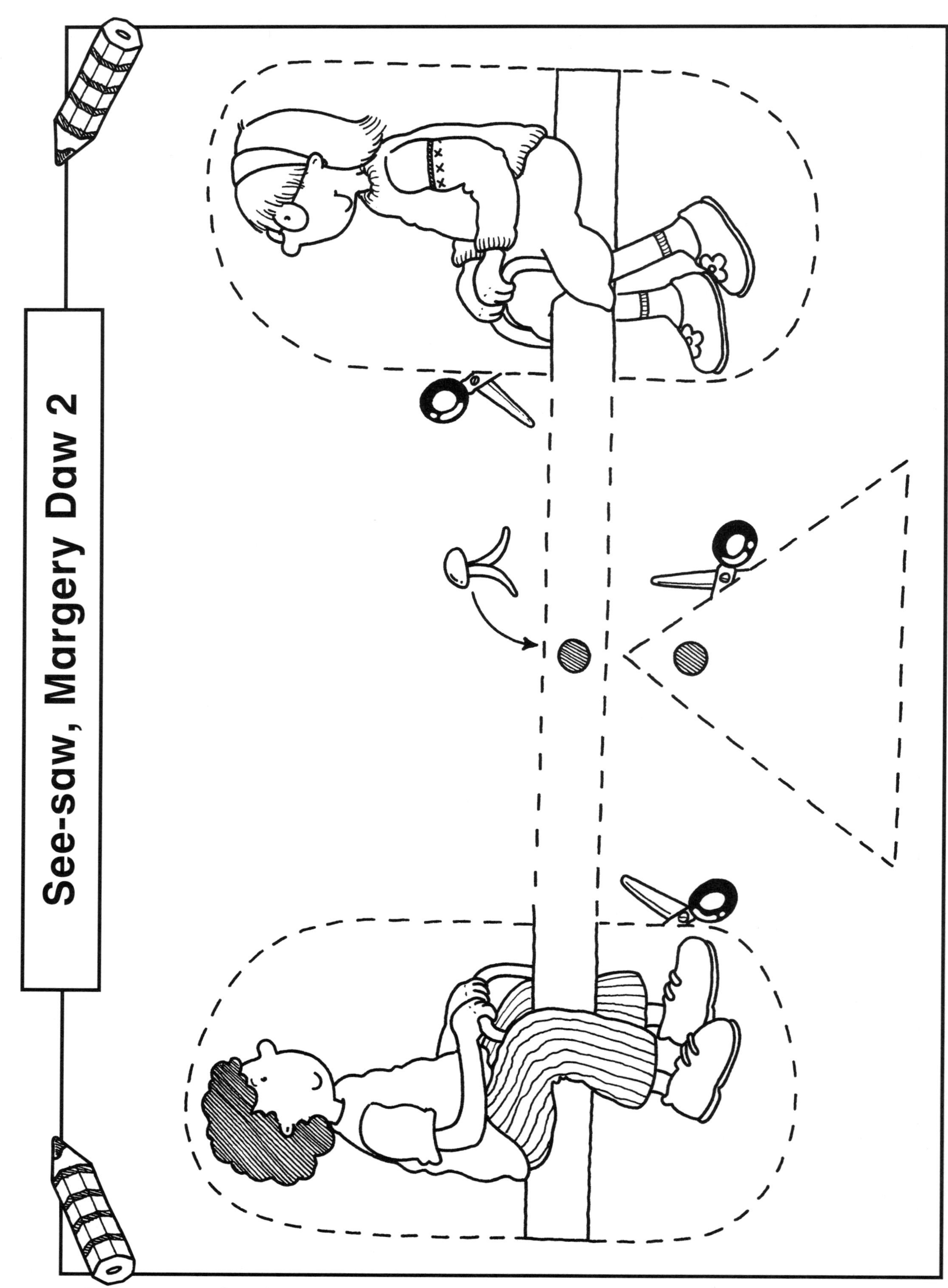

Teachers' note Use this with page 11. Copy the page on to card and give to the children to cut around the dotted lines. Fix the see-saw to the base using a split pin as a pivot.

Pat-a-cake, pat-a-cake

• **Say the rhyme.**

Clap the rhythm.

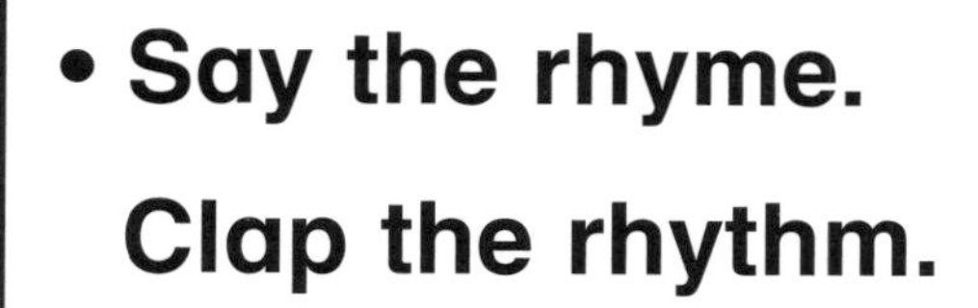

The hands show you when to clap.

Pat - a - cake, pat - a - cake, baker's man,

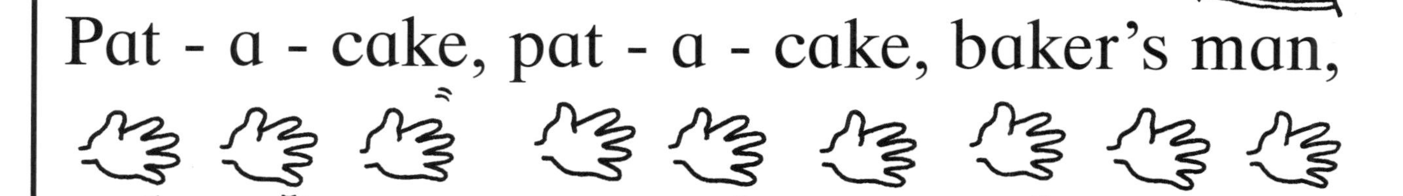

Bake me a cake as fast as you can;

Pat it and prick it, and mark it with B;

Put it in the oven for Baby and me.

• **Learn the rhyme.**

Look and read **Cover** **Say** **Check**

Teachers' note Although the children will not have learned about syllables, most of them will be able to clap their hands to each beat of this simple rhythm (the hands depicted beneath the words will help). Read the rhyme aloud, clapping your hands (the children clapping, too) and stop part-way through a line. Ask the children which word you have stopped on.

A hand mime

- **Say the rhyme.**

Do the actions.

Here are the lady's knives and forks,

Here is the lady's table,

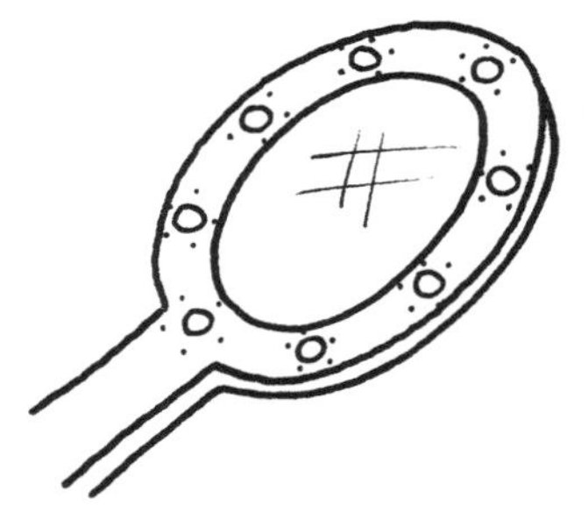

Here is the lady's looking-glass,

And here is the baby's cradle.

- **Learn the rhyme.**

Look and read **Cover** **Say** **Check**

Teachers' note Read the rhyme aloud with the children; demonstrate the hand mime and encourage the children to try it. They could mime one line of the rhyme for a friend to identify and recite.

A finger rhyme

- **Say the rhyme.**

  Use the finger puppets.

Two little dicky birds
Sitting on a wall,

One named Peter

And one named Paul.

Fly away, Peter!

Fly away, Paul!

Come back, Peter!

Come back, Paul!

- **Change the rhyme.**

  Use different finger puppets.

Teachers' note Use this page with the finger puppets on page 16. Many children will already know this familiar rhyme; encourage them to recite it and do the actions: they begin with a 'dicky bird' finger puppet on each hand, hold up each one as it is introduced (making it look as if it is sitting on a wall), then they make the birds fly away and come back.

Finger puppets

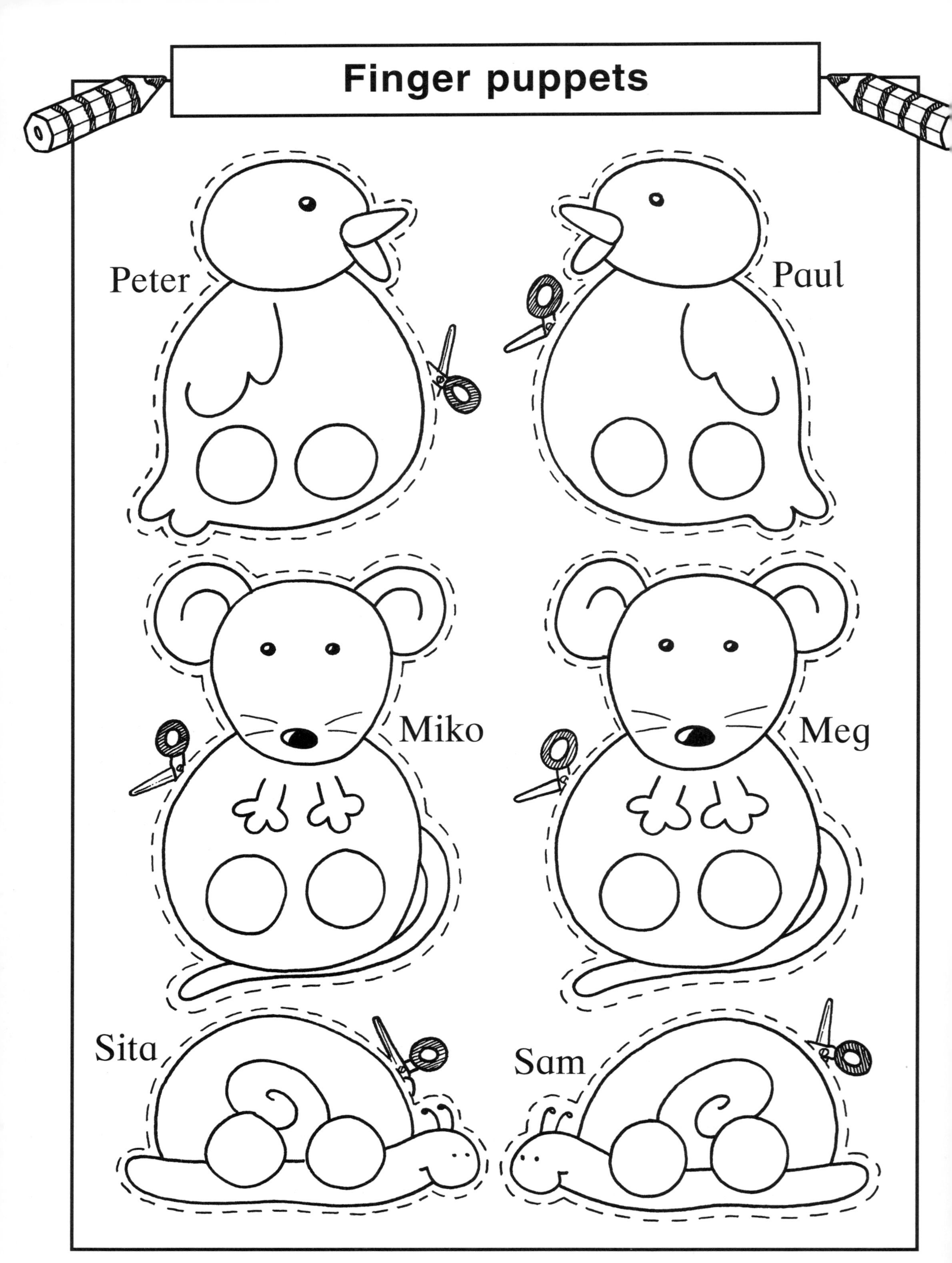

Teachers' note Use these finger puppets with page 15. Copy the page on to card and give to the children to cut out the outlines. They will need help in cutting the finger holes (see **Introduction** page 7 for a simple way to cut them out). The children say their finger rhymes to a friend. Encourage them to try out their ideas aloud with the puppets.

The bird

• **Say the poem.**

Do the actions.

	Actions	
Here are the legs that walk along.		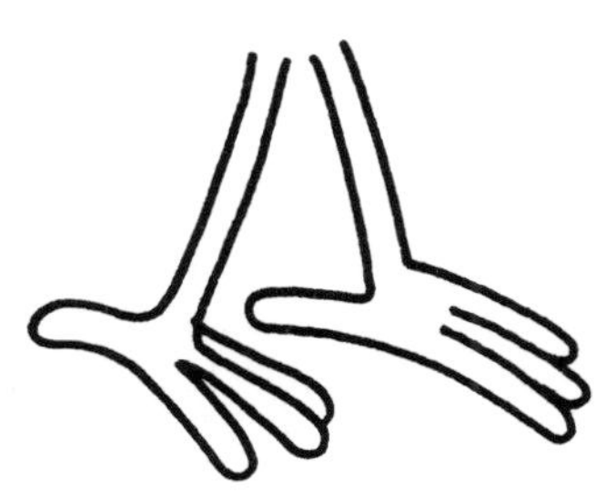
Here is the beak that sings a song.		
Here are the wings that flap and spread.		
And here is the bird above my head. Tony Mitton		

• **Cut out the words and pictures.**

• **Mix them up for a friend to match.**

Teachers' note The sections of the poem should not be cut out until the extension activity is reached. Read the poem aloud to the children; read it again and encourage them to join in and do the actions. Help them to memorise it (see **Introduction** page 5).

The cat

Make up a poem about a cat.

- **Choose words to fill the gaps.**
- **Do the actions.**

It doesn't have to rhyme.

 paws	Here are the ______________
pad pat tap	that ______________ ______________
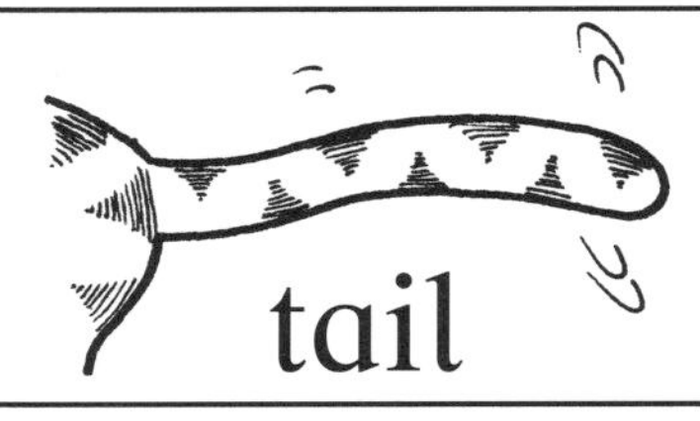 tail	Here is the ______________
flips flaps flicks	that ______________ ______________
 whiskers	Here are the ______________
tickle wiggle waggle	that ______________ ______________

- **Make up verses about the cat's**

ears **and** eyes.

Do the actions.

Teachers' note Discuss the movements of a cat to help the children choose the best word for the way in which it uses each part of its body. They should read their poems aloud, doing the actions. Examples of the responses which the children might make are: Here are the paws that pad along; Here is the tail that flicks the air; Here are the whiskers that tickle my face.

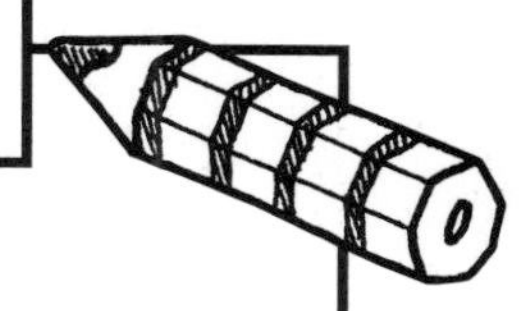

The elephant

Make up a poem about an elephant.

- **Fill in the gaps.**
- **Do the actions.**

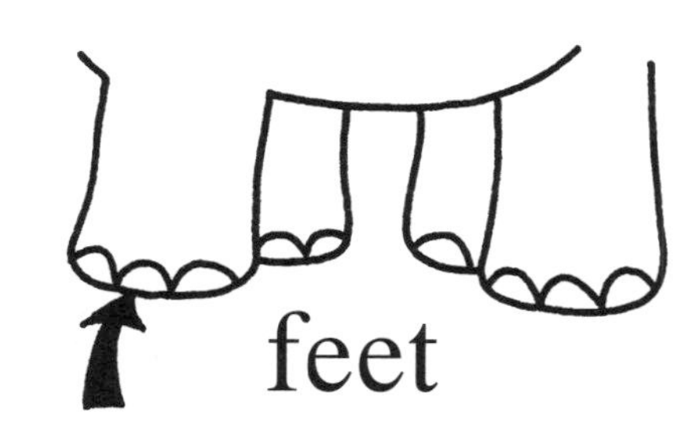

Here are the ________ that

____

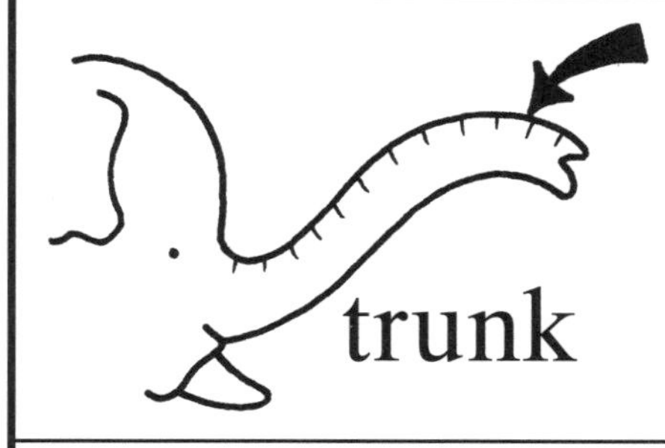

Here is the ________ that

____

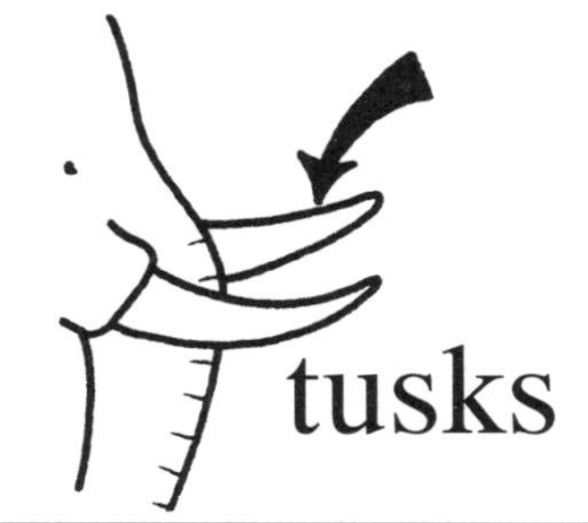

Here are the ________ that

____

Here is the ________ that

____

- **Make up a poem about another animal.**

Teachers' note Discuss the movements of an elephant to help the children choose the best word for the way in which it uses each part of its body. They should read their poems aloud, doing the actions. Examples of the responses which the children might make are: Here are the feet that stamp along; Here is the trunk that waves about.

Mix a pancake

- **Say the rhyme.**

Do the actions.

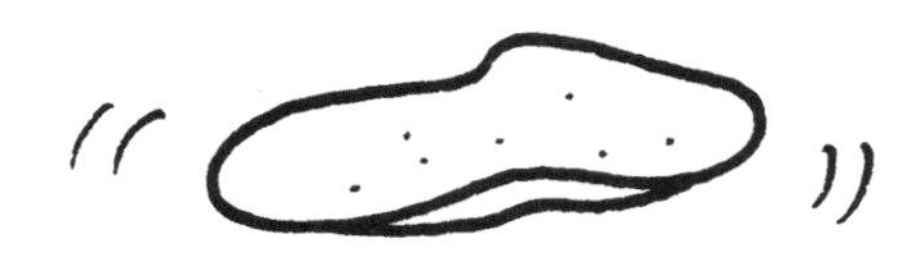

Mix a pancake,	stir a pancake,

pop it in a pan.	Fry the pancake,

toss the pancake,	catch it if you can!

- **Learn the rhyme.**

Look and read

Cover

Say
Check

Teachers' note Read the poem while enacting 'stirring' or 'mixing' pancake mixture; repeat the first two lines, while the children join in and mime the stirring of the pancake mixture, to help them appreciate its rhythm. Change the tone and rhythm of your voice to indicate the adventurous tossing of the pancake (look upwards for 'toss the pancake' and 'catch it if you can!').

Ring-a-ring o'roses

- **Say the rhyme.**

  Do the actions.

Ring-a-ring o'roses,
A pocket full of posies,
A-tishoo! A-tishoo!
We all fall down.

- **Make up two new endings.**
- **Draw the pictures.**

Ring-a-ring o'roses, A pocket full of posies, A-tishoo! A-tishoo! We all ________ ________.	
Ring-a-ring o'roses, A pocket full of posies, A-tishoo! A-tishoo! ______________________________	

- **Say the rhymes.**

  Do the actions.

Teachers' note The children could enact the rhyme if a large enough area is available; skipping in a ring to the first two lines and dropping to the ground for the next two. Encourage them to make up their own new endings orally, and enact them, before they begin the activity sheet.

Baa, baa, Black Sheep

- **Cut out the cards.**
- **Put them in order.**
- **Say the rhyme.**

Yes sir, yes sir,
Three bags full.

And one for the little boy
Who lives down the lane.

One for the master,
And one for the dame,

Baa, baa, Black Sheep,
Have you any wool?

- **Learn the rhyme.**

Look and read **Cover** **Say** **Check**

Teachers' note Introduce this activity by asking the children if they can recite *Baa, baa, Black Sheep*. Split the class into groups (or the group into pairs or individuals) and allocate two lines to each of them. The first group (or pair or individual) asks the question; the others, in turn, recite the replies.

What are children made of?

• **Say the rhyme.**

What are naughty children made of, made of?
What are naughty children made of?
Slugs and snails
And puppy-dogs' tails,
That's what naughty children are made of.

What are good children made of, made of?
What are good children made of?
Sugar and spice
And all things nice,
That's what good children are made of.

• **Learn the rhyme.**

Look and read **Cover** **Say** **Check**

• **What else could children be made of?**

• **Make up your own rhyme.**

Teachers' note Read the rhyme. Repeat it with the children joining in. They could read the rhyme with a friend; one asking the questions and the other giving the answers (using the words supplied on pages 24 and 25 and thinking up others of their own).

What are they made of? 1

Fish and chips

and apple pips

Plums and pears

and teddy bears

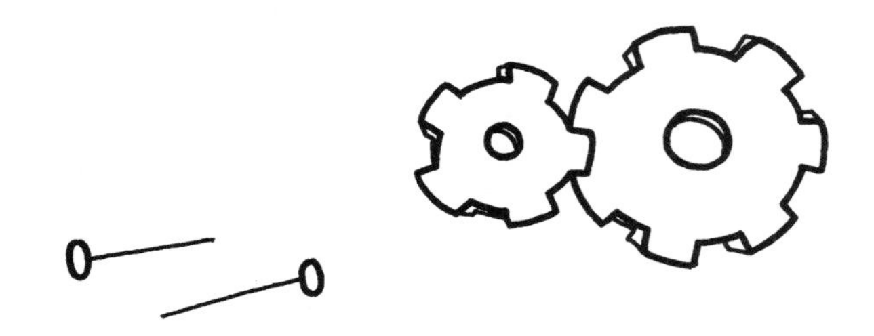

Pins and cogs

and pigs and hogs

The moon and stars

and candy bars

Teachers' note Cut the page into separate cards as indicated. Use the cards with pages 23 and 25. The cards could be mixed up and the children could find the matching rhyme for each one.

What are they made of? 2

Cats and dogs

and worms and frogs

Bugs and flies

and apple pies

Mops and rags

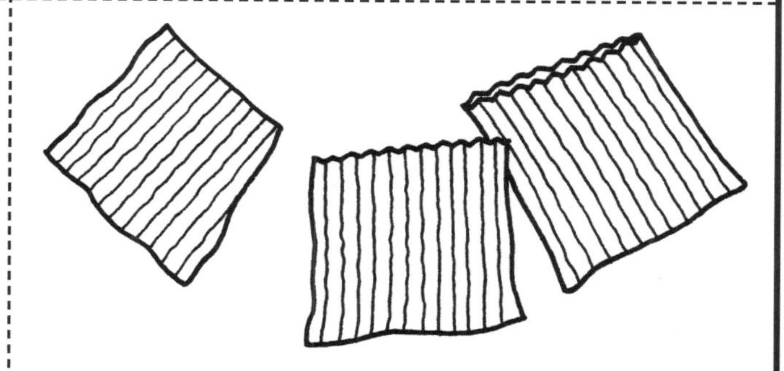

and paper bags

Big red rugs

and kisses and hugs

Teachers' note Cut the page into separate cards as indicated. Use the cards with pages 23 and 24.

What's the time, Mr Wolf?

- Fill in the gaps.
- Say the poem with your group.

Take turns to be the sheep and the wolf.

- Make up a new poem.
- Take turns to be the wolf.

Teachers' note For the extension activity provide some of the children (the wolves) in a group with clock faces with moveable hands. The other children take turns to ask one of the wolves the time, to develop the poem. They then swap roles and repeat. They could vary the poem by answering 'Bedtime' or 'Dinnertime'.

A mosquito one, a mosquito two

- **Say the rhyme. Do the actions.**

★ A mosquito one, a mosquito two, ★
A mosquito jump in the old man shoe. ★ ★

A mosquito three, a mosquito four,
A mosquito open the old man door.

A mosquito five, a mosquito six,
A mosquito pick up the old man sticks.

A mosquito seven, a mosquito eight,
A mosquito open the old man gate.

A mosquito nine, a mosquito ten,
A mosquito biting the man again.

- **Learn the rhyme.**

Look and read   Cover   Say   Check

- **Say the rhyme with a friend.**

Teachers' note Read the rhyme, showing the children how to make the numbers with their fingers and thumbs (as shown in the illustrations). Read it again, demonstrating when to slap the floor, clap hands or stamp feet on the beat (indicated by the stars). Read it once more: see if they can combine both actions – showing the numbers and slapping, clapping or stamping on the beat.

Find the rhyme

• **Match the numbers to the words.**

2
two

4
four

6
six

8
eight

10
ten

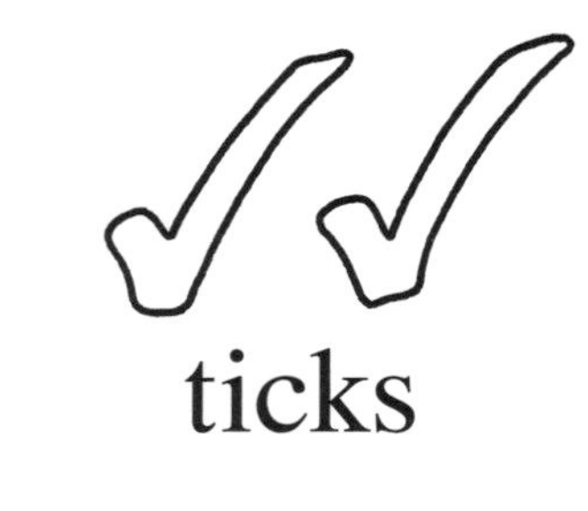

ticks

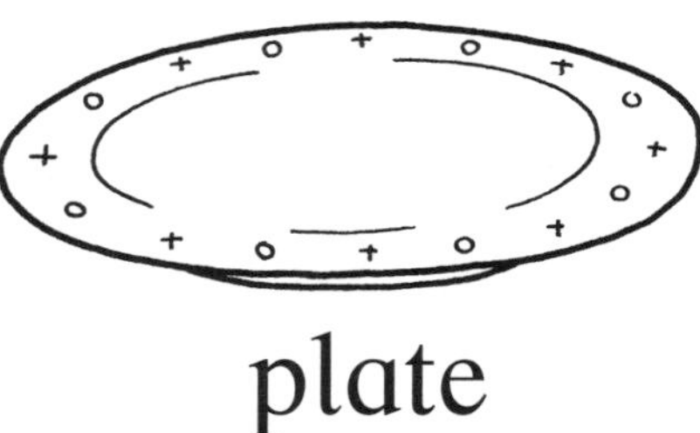

plate

hen

zoo

saw

• **With a friend, make up another mosquito rhyme.**

• **Say it together.**

Teachers' note The children should first do the activity on page 27. After finding the rhyming words for the numbers, the children make up their own versions of the rhyme *A mosquito one, a mosquito two*. Encourage them to show the numbers with their fingers and thumbs and slap, clap or stamp on the beat.

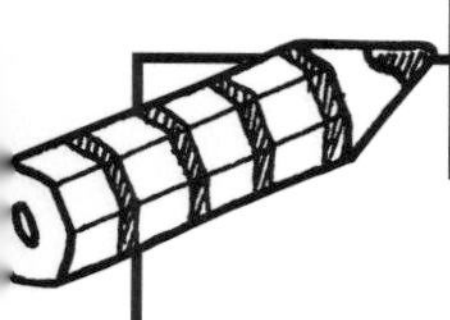

One potato, two potato

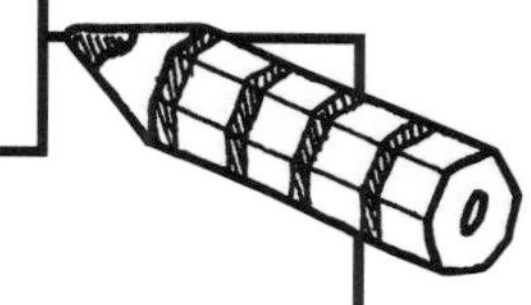

One potato, two potato,
Three potato, four,
Five potato, six potato,
Seven potato, more!

- **Say the rhyme.**
- **Say another food, instead of 'potato'.**

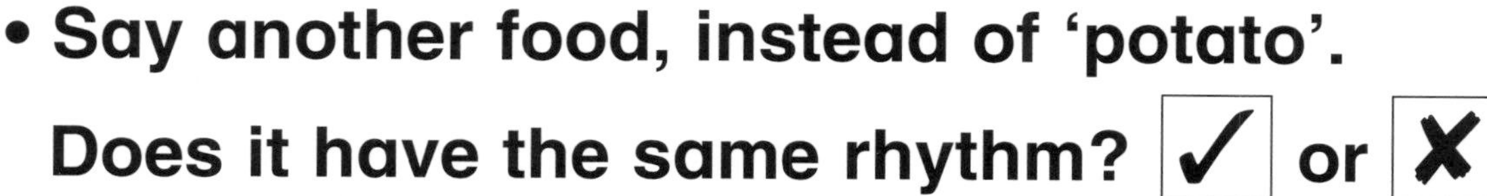

Does it have the same rhythm?   **or** 

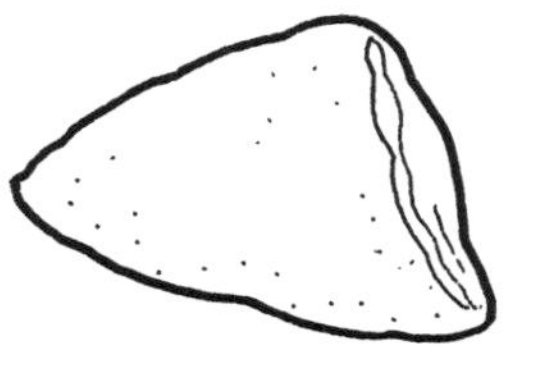

samosa banana cherry spaghetti

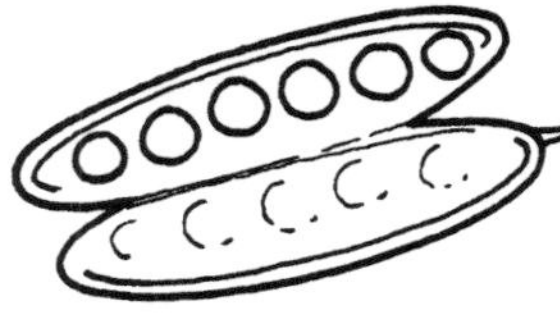
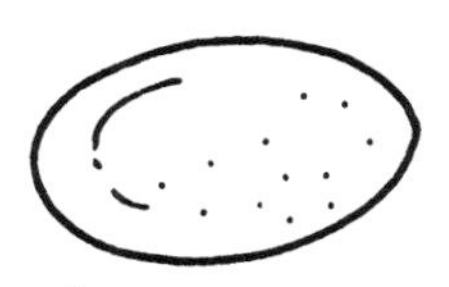

tomato pea chapatti pear

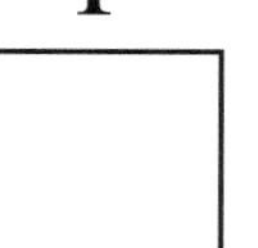

- **Say the rhyme with other foods.**
- **Draw and write the foods which have the same rhythm.**

Teachers' note After reading the rhyme, encourage the children to try out the names of the different foods in place of the word 'potato' and to say which ones sound right. Point out the rhythm. Other foods for their own rhymes include: fishfinger, chip butty, cream cracker and cheese sandwich.

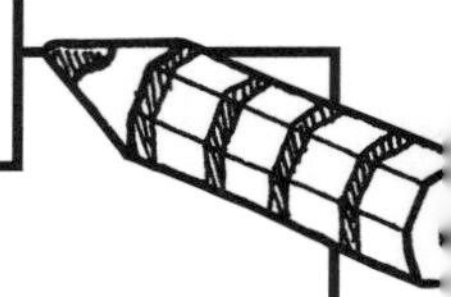

Eeny, meeny, miney, mo

- **Say the rhyme.**
- **On each word, point to a teddy bear.**
- **Which teddy bear do you finish on?** 

Eeny, meeny, miney, mo,

Catch a teddy by his toe;

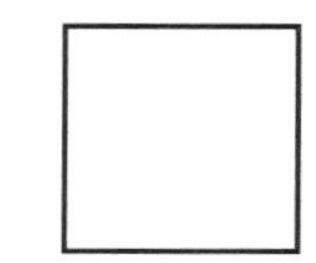

If he squeals, let him go,

Eeny, meeny, miney, mo.

- **Change the rhyme.**

Start and finish with Izzy bizzy buzzy bo...

Teachers' note Reciting this rhyme, the children could also play a game, using real teddy bears, in which the teddy bear to which they point at the end of the rhyme is eliminated. Some of them could invent their own choosing rhymes, based on the second and third lines of this one, but making up the first and fourth lines.

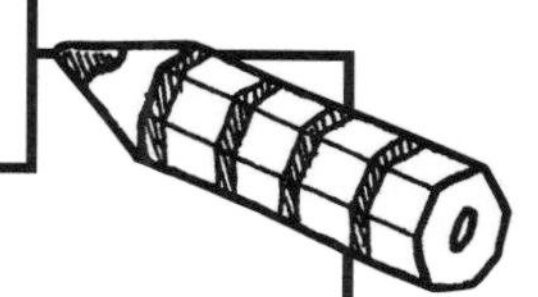

Alphabet rhymes

- Say the names of these letters.
- Join each letter in a circle to a word that rhymes.

d, e, f

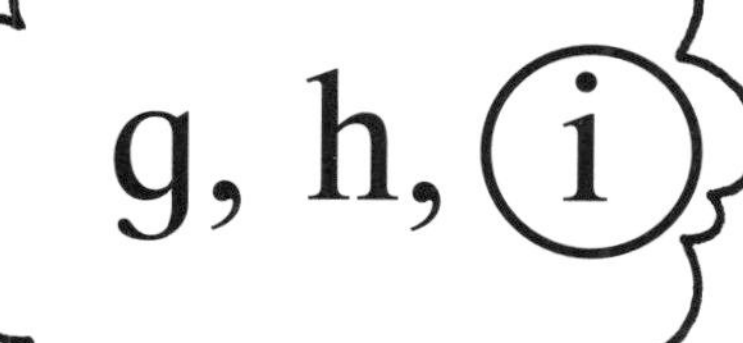

Here is a bell.

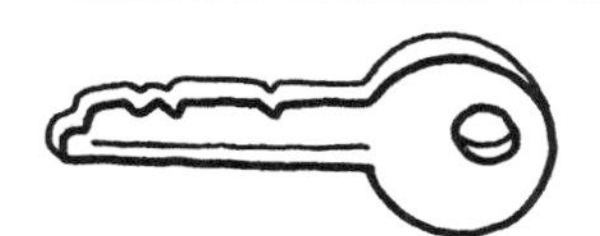

Here is a key.

Here is a car.

Here is Jeff.

Here is a pie.

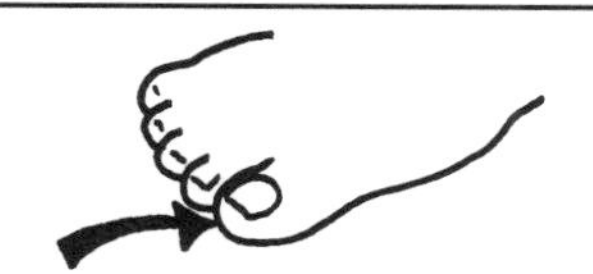

Here is a toe.

- Make up rhymes for these.

Teachers' note Most children should be able to work on this activity independently. The pictures and the repetition of 'Here is a …' help them to read it unaided, and provide a pattern which they can follow for their own alphabet rhyme. During the plenary session a group could recite the whole alphabet in rhyme.

Alphabet poem 1

a b c d e f g h i j k l m
n o p q r s t u v w x y z

- **With a friend, say and clap.**
- **Fill in the gaps.**

You say	Your friend says
Give me an 'a',	And go away!
Give me a _____ ,	And look at _________ .
Give me a _____ ,	And have some _________ .

Teachers' note Show the children how to clap on each syllable as they recite the invitation (You say) and response (Your friend says). Ask them to swap parts so that they each have a chance to make up the rhymes. Continued on page 33.

Teachers' note Use this with page 32. The children could continue through the alphabet (without necessarily writing each invitation and response). Different groups could work on different sets of letters so that, during the plenary session, the whole alphabet is recited with rhyming words for each letter.

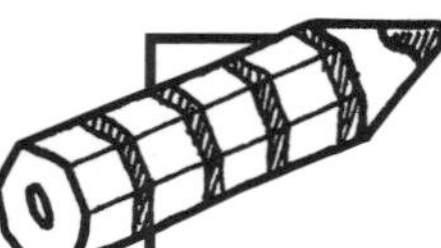

Ee-aye-addio

• **Say the football song.**

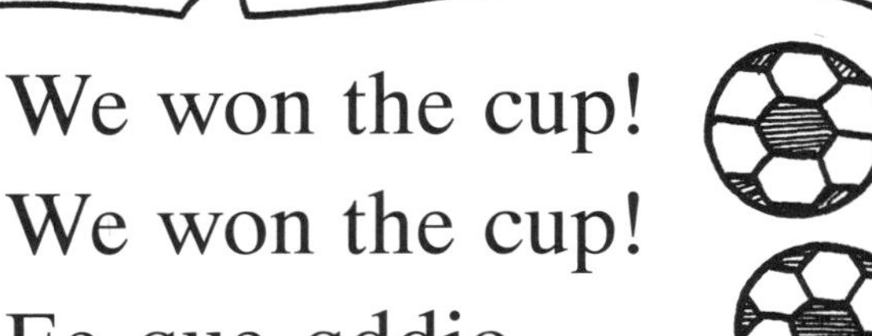

We won the cup!
We won the cup!
Ee-aye-addio,
We won the cup!

• **Fill in the gaps.**

We want a goal!
We want a goal!

____

____

What a great shot!
What a great shot!

____

____

• **Say the song.**

• **Make up another verse for the song.**

Teachers' note Different groups could recite or sing the verses of the football song, including any they have made up, with the whole class joining in the chorus.

Polly put the kettle on

- **Say the poem.**
- **Fill in the gaps.**

Polly put the kettle on,

Polly put the kettle on,

Polly put ______________________ ,

We'll all have tea.

Sukey take it off again,

Sukey ______________________ ,

______________________ ,

They've all gone away.

- **Make up other verses.**

Becky bake some biscuits,

Teachers' note Read the poem to the children and then repeat it, stopping for them to supply the repeated words. In the extension activity encourage them to read and repeat the first lines provided. They should re-read the last line of each of the previous verses before making up their own.

Ee-aye-ee-aye-o 1

- **Say the chorus.**

Ee-aye-ee-aye-o!

- **Say the verse.**
- **Write each chorus.**

Old MacDonald had a farm,

And on that farm he had a cow,

With a moo-moo here and a moo-moo there,
Here a moo, there a moo,
Everywhere a moo-moo,
Old MacDonald had a farm,

Teachers' note The poem can be read by the whole class, in groups, with an adult reading the first line, the whole class joining in the chorus, individuals introducing each animal and their own group making the sound of the animal. Continued on page 37.

Ee-aye-ee-aye-o 2

Old MacDonald had a farm,

And on that farm he had a hen,

With a cluck-cluck here and a

______________________________ ,

Here a ____________ , there a ____________ ,

Everywhere a ____________________ ,

Old MacDonald had a farm,

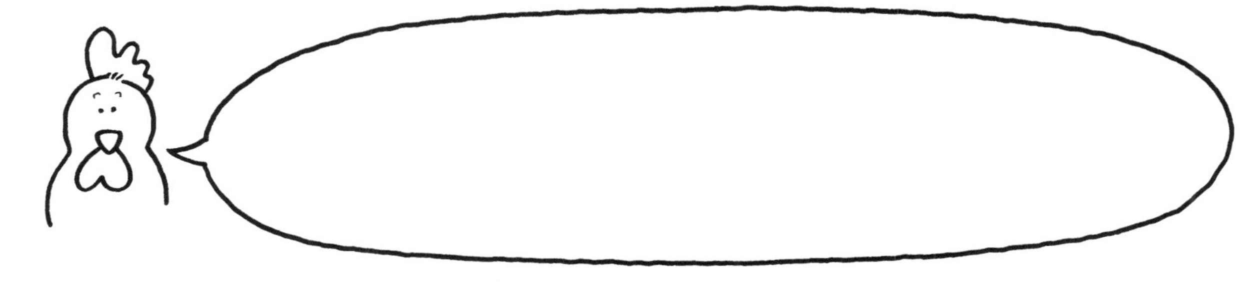

- **Make up verses for these.**

a sheep

a duck

a horse

- **Say your verses to a friend.**

Teachers' note Use this with page 36. Individuals could read the verses they have made up, with the whole class joining in the chorus.

Messy mud

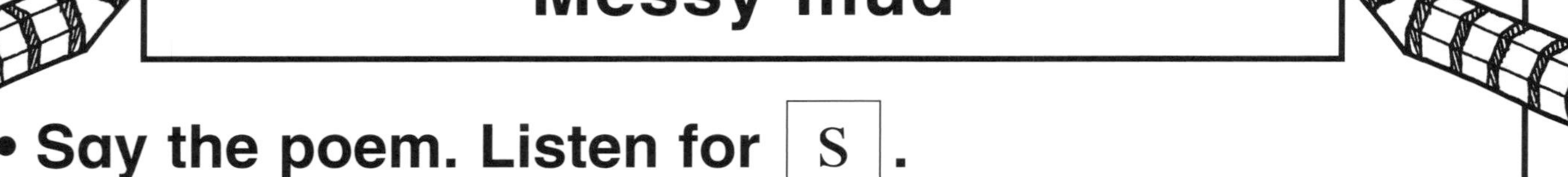

- Say the poem. Listen for s.
- Circle the words with s.

I like mud.
The slippy, sloppy,
squelchy kind,
The slap-it-into-pies kind.
Stir it up in puddles,
Slither and slide.
I *do* like mud.

Shirley Hughes

- Say the poem again.

  Listen for p.
- Write the words with p.

______________ ______________ ______________

______________ ______________ ______________

- Make up your own 'mud' words.

  Use s and p.
- Say your words to a friend.

Teachers' note Read the poem to the children (it is not intended that they should try to read it for themselves, although many of them will manage the first and last lines). Re-read it, pausing for the children to repeat each line. Ask them what they notice about the sounds (the words sound like mud squelching).

Teachers' note Read the words 'crispy crunchy' and ask the children to repeat them over again. Do they think the words sound crispy and crunchy? Which things in the pictures are 'crispy crunchy'? Other things the children might include are: cream crackers, biscuits, dry leaves, gravel, shells, toast and popcorn.

Thump, bump

- **Take turns to roll the dice.**
- **Move your counter.**
- **Look and read.**

Does it go 'thump, bump'?

yes **roll the dice again**

no **stop**

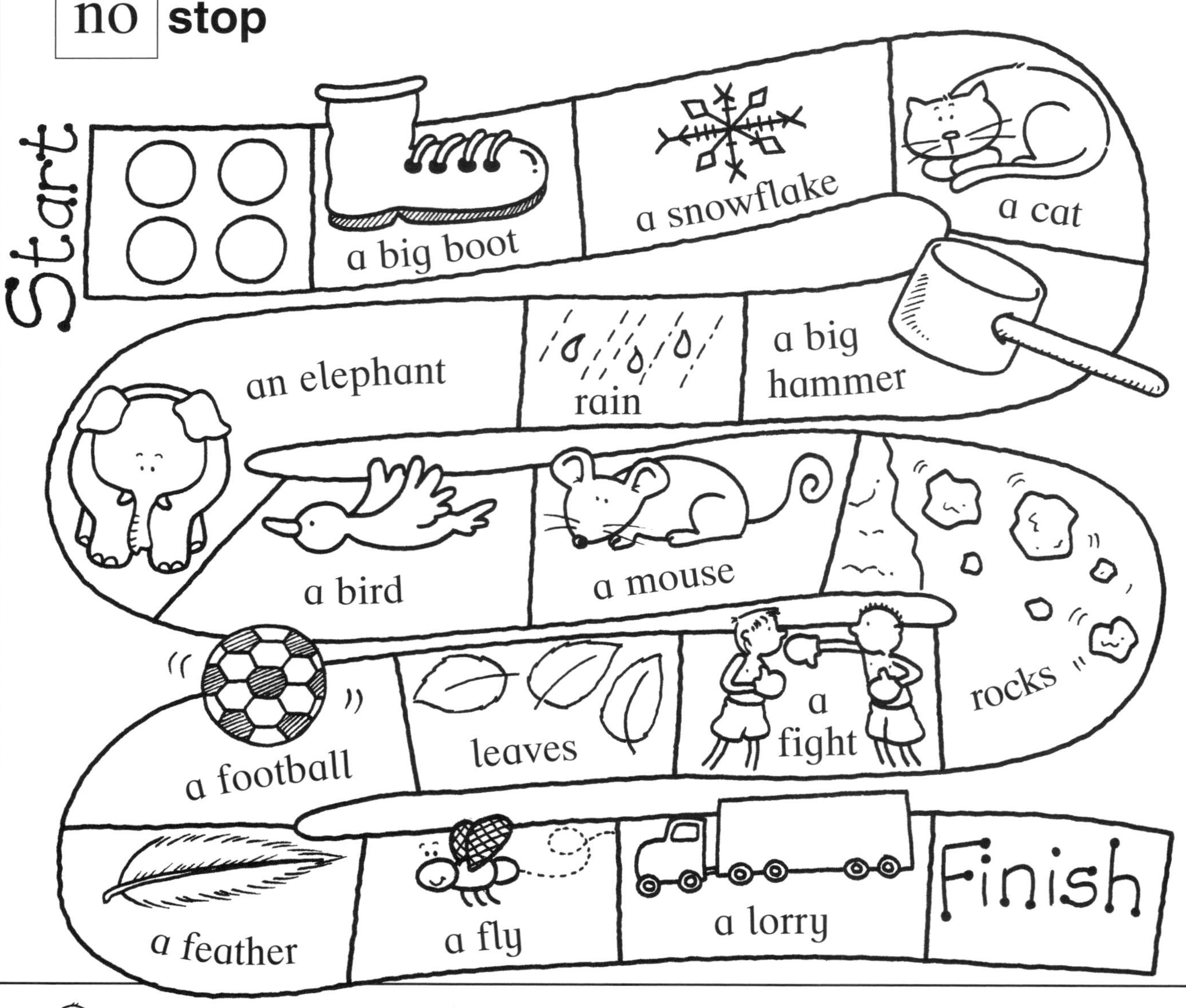

- **Draw and label two other things which go 'thump, bump'.**

Teachers' note This game for four players develops appreciation of the qualities of sounds. Introduce the activity with 'thump, bump' sounds by hitting a table top with the side of a fist. Look at the board game with the children and name the objects in turn. If its sound is 'thump, bump' the children shout 'THUMP, BUMP!'; if not, they whisper 'Not thump, bump'.

Crazy creatures

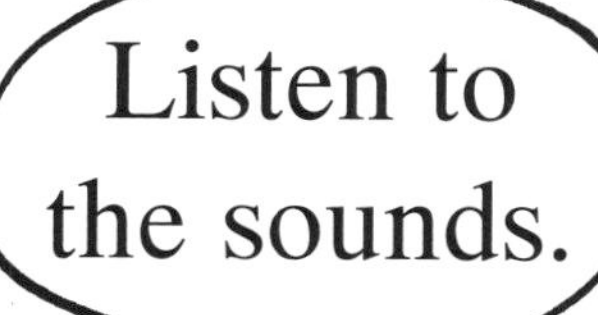

slimy snail

- **Write a word for each animal.**

Word-bank

buzzing
pink
red
wiggly

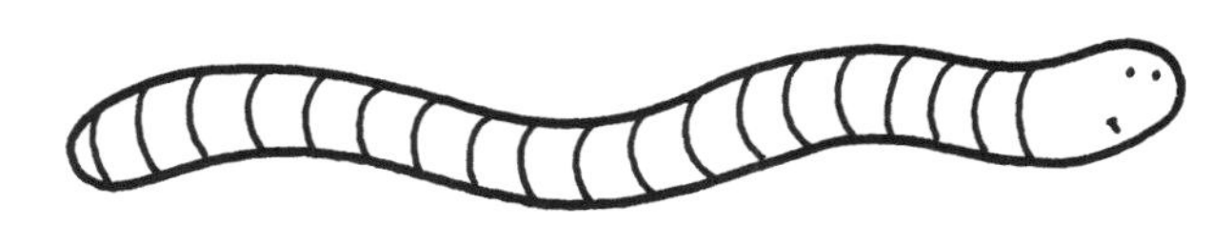

____

worm

____

robin

____

bee

____

pig

- **Write words for these.**

bird hen fish

Teachers' note With the children, read the words in the word-bank and the words for the animals, emphasising the initial consonants. Encourage them to repeat 'slimy snail' and to say what they notice about the sounds of the words.

Hop to the shop

- **Write words that rhyme.**

hop to the shop

Word-bank

hay
king
ship
sky
sun

skip to the ________________

run in the ____________

fly in the ____________

sing to the ____________

play in the ____________

- **Make up rhymes for these.**

go	hug	fall	drink

Teachers' note Ask the children what they notice about the sounds of 'time for a rhyme' and 'hop to the shop'. After they have completed the activity sheet, encourage them to read and repeat each rhyming sound they have written. They could think of alternative rhyming words: for example, hop with a mop and run with a bun.

Sound pictures

drums

trotting horse

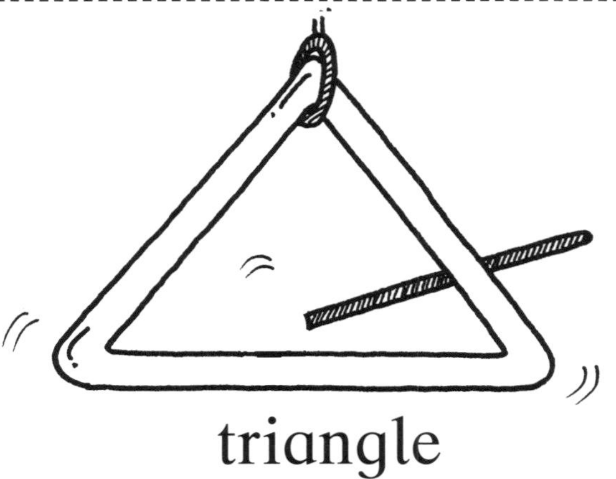

triangle

paintbrush

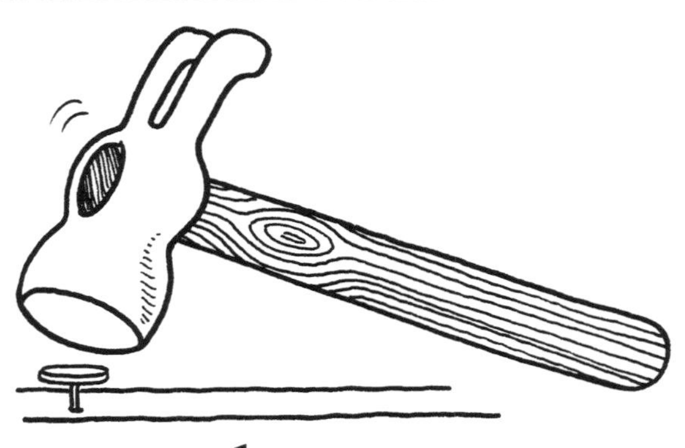

hammer

police car

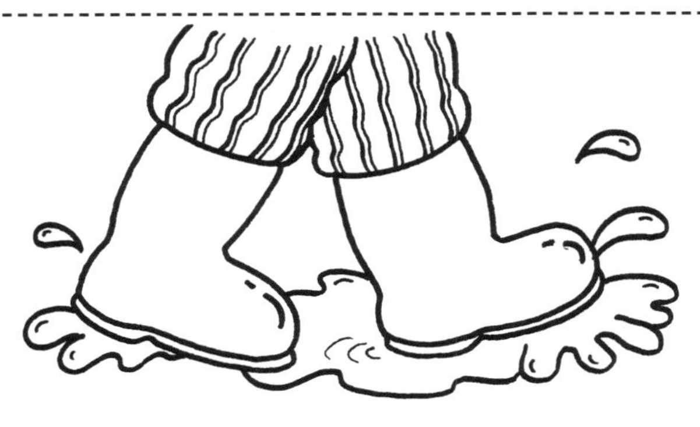

boots in puddles

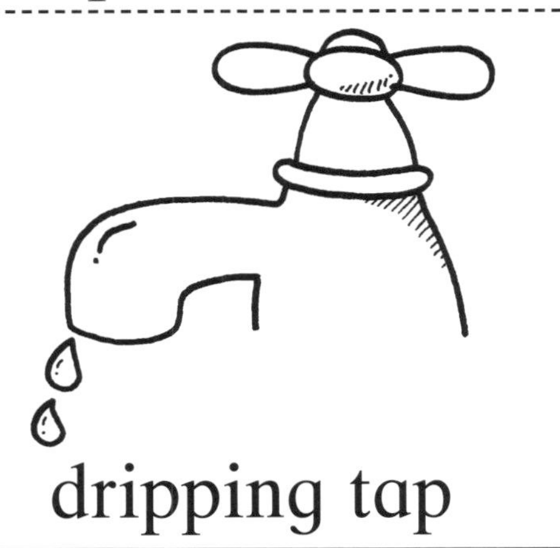

dripping tap

Teachers' note Use this with page 44. The children cut out the sound pictures and, working with a partner or in a small group, match them to the sound cards. They could also play 'matching pairs' with both sets of cards: spread them out face down and ask the children to take turns to turn over two cards. If the sound matches the picture, they keep the pair.

Sound cards

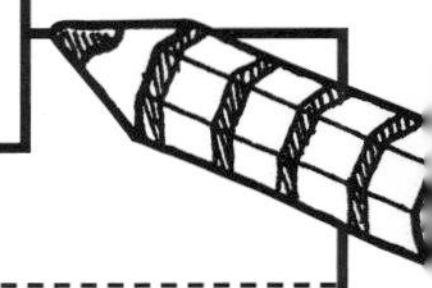

da da dum, da da dum	clip, clop, clip, clop
ting, tang, ting, tang	slop, slap, slop, slap
tap, tap tap, tap	nee-na, nee-na
splish, splosh splish, splosh	drip, drop drip, drop

Teachers' note Use this with page 43. The children cut out the sound cards and match them to the pictures. Ask them to read the sounds by sounding out the letters.

Animal sounds

• **Join the animals to the sounds.**

• **Make sounds for other animals.**

• **Ask a friend to guess what they are.**

Teachers' note If possible, combine this activity with observations of real animals, or recordings of them. The children can listen to the sound of each animal and make the sound themselves. They could also make up silly rhymes about the animals: for example, 'Woof,' said the dog as he chopped a log; 'Meow,' said the cat as she put on her hat.

Outdoor sounds

• Join the pictures to the sounds.

• Say the sounds for other things.

• Ask a friend to guess what they are.

Teachers' note If possible, combine this activity with a walk around the local area, or let the children listen to recordings of sounds heard outdoors. The children can listen to each sound and then try to make the sound themselves.

Morning and night poems 1

- Cut out the cards.
- Make up a morning poem.
- Make up a night poem.
- Say your poems.

Sleep

Breakfast

Upstairs

Brush teeth

Sleepy head

Time to go out

Tea

Time to come in

Teachers' note Use this with page 48. Ask the children (working with a partner or in a small group) to sort the cards into 'morning' and 'night'. Some of the cards could be placed in either set: encourage the children to discuss their sorting and to say why the cards belong in a particular set.

Morning and night poems 2

Good morning

Good night

Wash face

Downstairs

Bedtime story

Bedtime clothes

Bath-time

Wake up

Toast

Off to school

Teachers' note Use this with page 47. When the children have sorted the cards, ensure that they can read the words on them. They choose some of them to arrange as a poem (you could limit them to four or five cards). Ask them to read their poems aloud and to decide if they want to change them.